To My Child

_____

With Love From

_____

Date

_____

A Mother's Memories

A Keepsake Book

GEORGENE MULLER LOCKWOOD

PUBLICATIONS INTERNATIONAL, LTD.

Georgene Muller Lockwood is a freelance magazine and newspaper writer whose work has appeared in *Modern Bride* and *Working Woman*. She is the author of *Your Victorian Wedding: A Modern Guide for the Romantic Bride*.

Louis Weber, C.E.O.
Publications International, Ltd.
7373 North Cicero Avenue
Lincolnwood, IL 60646

CONTENTS

A GIFT OF MEMORIES

This is a book about us. It's about me...where I've come from, who I've known,
what I've done, the things I've seen. Perhaps some things you experienced growing up
will make more sense to you now, when you read these pages filled with memories and
expressions of the things I hold dearest to my heart.

But this book is about you, too. It's about your childhood and what I remember
most about our time together as a family. It's about the many important events, people,
and places that collectively have helped to make you the wonderful
human being you've become.

This is our record for posterity. Not just a family history, but a personal journey into the
past with a view to the future. I hope it's something even more. It's a book about the
things that endure for all time: family, friendship, learning, growth, joy, and love.
Most of all, the pages of this book are filled with love. Now it's up to you to pass it on.

DEAR ONES

Kindred Spirits

A family is a group of people linked by birth who have learned to
live together even though they may be as different as strangers. Yet the magic bond
of blood and shared experience binds us no matter how far we stray. You will see your
family through my recollections and through my particular eyes. This isn't the whole story,
but it's the one I know. We are all a part of you, and you bring us with you into the
future. When you raise your own family, you will look back on our family, and
it will all make a new sense to you.

In a typical day, I remember my mother doing _____

_____.

What I remember most about the way my mother looked when she was young is

_____.

My father's occupation was _____.

My mother's occupation was _____.

One special memory I have of my mother is _____

_____.

One special memory I have of my father is _____

_____.

The member of the family most people say I take after is _____.

You get _____ from your

father's side of the family. You get _____ from

my side of the family.

When I was a boy of fourteen, my father was so ignorant I could hardly
stand to have the old man around. But when I got to be twenty-one, I was
astonished at how much he had learned in seven years.

Mark Twain

Family Favorites

Some relatives who were not part of our immediate family had a place like no other. My favorite aunt always knows exactly the right thing to send for my birthday, and I can tell her things I cannot tell anyone else. And my cousins brought their own special brand of mischief when they came to visit. Cultivating and nurturing relationships from the farther branches of the family tree makes us richer and adds another, deeper dimension.

MY FAVORITE AUNT IS _____ BECAUSE _____

_____.

MY FAVORITE UNCLE IS _____ BECAUSE

_____.

WHEN MY COUSINS VISITED WE PLAYED _____.

WHEN OUR FAMILY GOT TOGETHER FOR IMPORTANT OCCASIONS, THE

PEOPLE WHO USUALLY WERE THERE WERE _____

_____.

THE FAMILY GATHERING I REMEMBER BEST IS _____.

THE MEMBER OF OUR EXTENDED FAMILY YOU TOOK A SPECIAL SHINE TO WHEN YOU WERE

GROWING UP WAS _____. I KNEW THIS BECAUSE

_____.

THE INCIDENT I REMEMBER BEST ABOUT YOU AND A MEMBER OF OUR EXTENDED FAMILY

IS _____.

What families have in common the world around is that they are the place
where people learn who they are and how to be that way.

Jean Illsley Clarke

Family Friends

When I was very small, we regularly saw one couple in church. They were family friends, but to me they were mostly like grandparents, especially the man, whom I would even call "Papa." During the long services, when it was so hard for an energetic little one to sit still and remain silent, Papa would set me on his knee and bring me sheets of colored paper and pencils to scribble with. The time seemed to pass more swiftly. Each Sunday we'd look for one another. I will never forget him and his kindness that always meant so much to a little girl who got the wiggles in church.

WHEN I WAS GROWING UP, FRIENDS OF OUR FAMILY WERE _____.

ACTIVITIES WE DID TOGETHER WITH OTHER FAMILIES INCLUDED _____
_____.

MY CLOSEST FRIEND WHEN YOU WERE GROWING UP WAS _____. WHAT I

REMEMBER MOST ABOUT HER IS _____.

YOUR DAD'S GREATEST FRIENDS WHEN YOU WERE GROWING UP WERE _____
_____.

SOME THINGS THEY'D DO TOGETHER WERE _____

_____.

YOUR "COURTESY" AUNT, WHOM YOU CALLED "AUNT" THOUGH SHE WASN'T A RELATIVE,

WAS _____. SHE USED TO TAKE YOU TO _____

_____.

YOUR "COURTESY" UNCLE WAS _____. HE USED TO

BRING YOU _____.

OUR BEST NEIGHBORS ARE _____. WE WOULD HELP

EACH OTHER OUT BY _____.

I WOULD INDUCT _____ INTO THE BABY-SITTER'S HALL OF

FAME; SHE WAS ALWAYS ABLE TO KEEP YOU AMUSED BY _____

_____.

Best Friends

How the miracle of friendship happens will remain ever a mystery to me. I think there are friends for different parts of a person—some to have fun with, some for sorrow, some who are intellectual partners, and others who share beliefs and aspirations. Rare, indeed, is that one person who is a friend in all of these ways. Should you find one, know that you have found a treasure for all time.

Friends cherish each other's hopes,
They are kind to each other's dreams.

Henry David Thoreau

THE EARLIEST FRIEND I REMEMBER HAVING IS _____.

MY BEST FRIEND IN GRAMMAR SCHOOL WAS _____. WE USED

TO _____ TOGETHER.

MY BEST FRIEND IN HIGH SCHOOL WAS _____. THE THINGS I

LIKED BEST ABOUT HER WERE _____, AND OUR FAVORITE

THINGS TO DO TOGETHER WERE _____.

MY BEST FRIEND IN COLLEGE WAS _____. OUR RELATIONSHIP

WAS SPECIAL BECAUSE _____

_____.

I EXCHANGED A TOKEN OF FRIENDSHIP WITH _____. WE GAVE

EACH OTHER _____.

THE CHILDREN IN MY NEIGHBORHOOD I PLAYED WITH WERE _____

_____.

OUR FAVORITE THINGS TO PLAY WERE _____

_____.

CHILDHOOD FRIENDS I'VE KEPT UP WITH ARE _____

_____. TODAY

THEY LIVE IN _____.

MY CLOSEST FRIENDS NOW ARE _____. THEY'RE

SPECIAL TO ME BECAUSE _____

_____.

MY FRIEND _____ HAD THE BIGGEST IMPACT ON ME WHILE

GROWING UP BECAUSE _____

_____.

THE FIRST CHILD I REMEMBER YOUR BECOMING FRIENDLY WITH WAS _____

_____.

YOUR NEIGHBORHOOD FRIENDS WERE _____

_____.

YOU WOULD ALL PLAY _____.

YOUR CLOSEST FRIEND IN SCHOOL WAS _____.

A FAVORITE SNAPSHOT OF

FRIENDS TOGETHER

My friends are my estate.

Emily Dickinson

Heroes

Heroes are created from a contract between the admired and the admirer. The admirer agrees to see only the best in their hero and use it as a beacon for goodness in life. The admired one needs to be consistent and true, but cannot be without flaws. No human, even a hero, is perfect. Heroes are not found just in our larger society. We should also look for them close by. The best heroes are the ones we know well enough to see their defects and still find in them much to be admired.

Heroes take journeys, confront dragons, and discover the treasure of their true selves.

Carol Pearson

_____ WAS A PERSON MY PARENTS GREATLY

ADMIRED, BECAUSE _____.

I DEFINE A HERO AS _____.

_____ IS THE PERSON IN PUBLIC LIFE I MOST

ADMIRE TODAY. WHAT MAKES ME FEEL THIS WAY IS _____.

THE PERSON I AM MOST INSPIRED BY IS _____, BECAUSE _____

_____.

THE PERSON FROM WHOM I'VE LEARNED THE MOST ABOUT LIFE IS _____

_____.

AMONG THE MOST IMPORTANT THINGS I'VE LEARNED IS _____

_____.

SOMEONE WHOSE LIFE I WOULD LIKE TO EMULATE IS _____,

BECAUSE _____.

MY FAVORITE FICTIONAL HERO HAS ALWAYS BEEN _____.

YOUR FAVORITE CHILDHOOD FICTIONAL HERO WAS _____.

PERSONAL CHARACTERISTICS AND TRAITS IMPORTANT TO YOU WERE _____

_____.

AN OLDER CHILD YOU LOOKED UP TO WHEN YOU WERE LITTLE WAS _____.

THE GROWNUP YOU ALWAYS ADMIRED WAS _____.

PLACES OF THE HEART

Home and Hearth

I went back to visit the first house I lived in as a child. The current owners were kind enough to let me in, and I climbed those familiar stairs to pay a brief visit to my old dormer bedroom. How strange it felt looking out those same windows I looked out so many years ago! I saw the cupboards where I kept my dolls, the odd angles of the ceiling. Everything appeared to be in miniature—the house itself seemed so small compared with the picture I'd held in my mind. But the view from the window was almost the same. The wisteria still bloomed; the grass still grew as green. Only the maple tree in the yard had grown up, as I had.

MY FATHER CAME FROM _____, AND MY MOTHER CAME FROM

_____. I WAS BORN IN THE TOWN OF _____,

AND THE FIRST HOUSE I LIVED IN WAS _____.

WHAT I REMEMBER ABOUT MY CHILDHOOD NEIGHBORHOOD IS _____

_____.

MY CHILDHOOD BEDROOM LOOKED LIKE _____

_____.

THE FIRST PLACE I LIVED WHEN I LEFT MY FAMILY HOME WAS _____.

WHAT I RECALL ABOUT IT IS _____

_____.

THE FIRST PLACE YOUR FATHER AND I LIVED IN AFTER WE WERE MARRIED WAS _____

_____. THE FIRST HOUSE WE BOUGHT WAS _____

_____.

WHEN YOU WERE BORN, WE LIVED IN _____.

YOUR CHILDHOOD BEDROOM HAD _____

_____.

School Days

Have you ever noticed that there's a definite school smell? All the schools I've ever been in had a variation of that smell. I've always wondered what ingredients made up that distinguishing odor of education. Chalk? Books? The janitor's mysterious solutions? The sweat and toil of children learning? You just can't mistake it, and after all the sweet smells of summer faded into September, that smell alerted you that unbridled play was about to give way to serious study once again. I call it eau de school, and it hasn't changed in at least 40 years.

WHAT I REMEMBER MY MOTHER SAYING ABOUT HER SCHOOL DAYS IS _____

_____.

ONE STORY MY FATHER TELLS ABOUT HIS SCHOOL DAYS IS _____

_____.

THE FIRST SCHOOL I WENT TO WAS _____.

THE PLAYGROUND HAD _____,

AND WE PLAYED _____.

I WENT TO HIGH SCHOOL AT _____ IN THE

TOWN OF _____. I GOT THERE BY _____.

I WENT TO COLLEGE AT _____ IN _____.

THE CAMPUS WAS _____.

ONE OF MY SCHOOLMATES WHO BECAME FAMOUS IS _____.

WHAT I REMEMBER ABOUT YOUR FIRST DAY OF SCHOOL AT _____

IS _____.

YOUR FAVORITE TEACHER WAS _____. THE SUBJECT YOU

LIKED BEST WAS _____.

WHEN YOU FIRST WENT AWAY TO SCHOOL, YOU FELT _____.

Maroon and White 1960

There are few of us who cannot remember a front-yard garden which seemed
to us a very paradise in childhood.

Sarah Orne Jewett

A Place to Frolic

Children find their own play places. Grown-ups make play places like parks and playgrounds, but the ones kids find for themselves are special. The sturdy arms of an aged oak, the front stoop that's "safe" or "home" in the after-dinner games, an unfinished basement just tailored for horseplay on a rainy day…these are the places to frolic.

WHEN I WAS A SMALL CHILD, I LIKED TO PLAY IN _____.

WHEN I GOT OLDER, WE USED TO PLAY _____

IN _____.

MY FAVORITE INDOOR PLACE TO PLAY WAS _____.

ON THE PLAYGROUND, WE USED TO PLAY _____.

WHEN YOU WERE VERY SMALL, I USED TO TAKE YOU TO _____

TO PLAY.

YOU AND THE NEIGHBORHOOD KIDS USED TO PLAY _____

IN _____.

INDOORS, YOU AND YOUR BEST FRIEND PLAYED _____

IN _____.

Getting Away

I remember vacation mornings—very early, with the air cool and the stars
still bright and no one else awake. The evening before was spent carefully packing
the trunk, the luggage carrier on top of the car, and if we were going camping, the little
trailer that would merrily bounce behind. The cooler was filled with soft drinks
and treats. We kids marked out our territories in the back seat, and the dog
stretched out on the back ledge under the window with a deep, contented sigh.
With Dad in the driver's seat and Mom next to him looking at the map,
we'd drive off into the half-light of morning.

THE MOST IMPORTANT TRIP MY PARENTS EVER TOOK WAS TO _____.

THE FIRST VACATION I CAN REMEMBER WAS _____.

I MOST ENJOYED VISITING _____,

BECAUSE _____.

I WENT TO SUMMER CAMP IN _____. MY PARTICULAR FRIENDS THERE

WERE _____,

AND THE THINGS I REMEMBER MOST ABOUT THE EXPERIENCE ARE _____

_____.

MY FAVORITE WAY TO TRAVEL IS _____,

BECAUSE _____.

THE PLACE I'D MOST LIKE TO RETURN TO IS _____,

BECAUSE _____.

THE PLACE I'D MOST LIKE TO VISIT THAT I NEVER HAVE IS _____.

I'VE HEARD IT'S _____.

YOUR FIRST VACATION TRIP WAS TO _____.

WHEN WE WENT ON VACATION AS A FAMILY, YOU ALWAYS PACKED _____

TO PLAY WITH. YOUR FAVORITE GAME TO PLAY IN THE CAR WAS _____.

MY FAVORITE TRIP WITH YOU WAS _____.

A Place to Ponder

Where do you go when the world is too much with you? Is it a garden? A gallery? A library? Do you steal away to a spot by a cool stream, one perched on a mountain or one near the pounding ocean's waves? Everywhere I've lived I've always scouted out a special thinking place—actually several, depending on what kind of thinking might be in order. These places renew us and give us comfort. My advice is to find some, wherever you are, and keep them in reserve, like pennies in a jar collected for a rainy day. When you need a place to ponder or reflect, you'll know exactly where to go.

WHEN MY MOTHER WANTED TO BE ALONE, I USUALLY FOUND HER AT _____
_____.

WHEN I WAS A CHILD, MY THINKING PLACE WAS _____
_____.

NOW, MY FAVORITE PLACE TO GO FOR WORKING OUT PROBLEMS IS _____
_____.

WHEN I'M LOOKING FOR INSPIRATION, THE PLACE I NATURALLY GO TO IS _____
_____.

MY FAVORITE PLACE JUST TO BE ALONE IS _____.

WHEN YOU WERE LITTLE, YOU LIKED TO GO TO _____

WHEN YOU WANTED TO BE ALONE.

ONE OF YOUR SPECIAL OUTDOOR PLACES WHEN YOU WERE A CHILD WAS _____

_____.

YOUR FAVORITE SPOT FOR READING WAS _____.

TREASURED POSSESSIONS

Playthings

Although you had your share of manufactured cuddly, furry animals, your most intimate companion was a stuffed purple fabric owl crafted by a family friend. Nothing could take the place of "Owlie" for comfort in times of need or companionship in celebration. Filled with extra-soft stuffing, he was crunched and pounded, twisted and maimed, and washed and dried—all in the name of love.

The real character of a man is found out by his amusements.

Joshua Reynolds

MY MOTHER RECALLED PLAYING WITH _____

WHEN SHE WAS A CHILD. MY FATHER'S FAVORITE CHILDHOOD TOY

WAS _____.

AS A CHILD, I USED TO PLAY _____ WITH

MY MOTHER. MY FAVORITE CHILDHOOD TOY WAS _____.

I LIKED IT BEST BECAUSE _____.

MY BEST DOLL WAS GIVEN TO ME BY _____. SHE HAD

_____ HAIR AND LOOKED LIKE _____.

I PLAYED WITH HER UNTIL I WAS _____ YEARS OLD. THE NAME I GAVE HER WAS

_____.

MY FAVORITE STUFFED ANIMAL WAS _____. I NAMED HIM

_____. THE THING I REMEMBER MOST ABOUT HIM IS _____

_____.

YOUR FAVORITE STUFFED ANIMAL WAS _____. YOU NAMED HIM

_____ AND PLAYED WITH HIM UNTIL YOU WERE _____ YEARS OLD.

YOUR FAVORITE DOLL WAS _____, AND YOUR FAVORITE OUTFIT

FOR HER WAS _____.

MY FAVORITE GROWN-UP TOY IS MY _____.

YOUR FATHER'S IS HIS _____.

29

Fine Feathers

When you were little, I kept a box, a mystical box full of alternate identities, different every time although the props remained the same. In the box were hats and costume jewelry, old curtains and fabric that could be pinned around the waist or used as a shawl, high-heeled shoes, discarded makeup, gloves, and handbags. Any number of pretend people could emerge. What better occupation for a couple of restless sisters than to make another world for a few hours? Now the boxes are filled with scarves and hair combs, evening bags and shawls—finery for an evening out. You're a grown young woman now, and when you come to rummage through my boxes, the dressing up is serious business. It's no longer for play... or is it?

WHEN I THINK OF MY MOTHER, I THINK OF HER WEARING _____.

I WORE _____ TO SCHOOL MOST OF THE TIME.

TEENAGERS IN MY DAY HAD SOME CRAZY FASHION FADS, JUST AS THEY DO NOW. SOME

FADS I REMEMBER FROM WHEN I WAS A TEENAGER ARE _____

_____.

MY FIRST "ADULT" CLOTHES WERE _____,

WHICH I GOT WHEN I WAS _____ YEARS OLD.

MY FAVORITE ARTICLE OF CLOTHING OF ALL WAS _____.

WHEN YOU WERE A SMALL CHILD, YOU LOOKED ABSOLUTELY ADORABLE IN _____

_____.

THE BEST HALLOWEEN COSTUME YOU EVER HAD WAS _____,

AND THE FUNNIEST WAS _____.

I REMEMBER A SCHOOL PLAY WHEN YOU PLAYED A _____ AND

WORE _____.

WHEN YOU WERE A TEENAGER, YOU ABSOLUTELY HAD TO HAVE A _____.

THE STYLE I MOST WISH THEY'D BRING BACK IS _____, BECAUSE

_____.

I hated to be grownup, and cried when I had my first long dress.

Kate Greenaway

Wheels

Once children discover that wheels can take them from here to there faster, life is never the same, either for them or for their parents. From the baby stroller onward to the scooter, the tricycle, roller skates, and the shiny new two-wheeler, the progression of wheels brings greater independence and more territory to conquer. And finally the long-awaited automobile confers the freedom and responsibility of adulthood.

I'm not sure where I'm going, but I'm making good time.

Jack McCormack

THE CAR I REMEMBER MY FAMILY HAVING WHEN I WAS A CHILD WAS A _____

_____ .

THE FIRST THING I REMEMBER PLAYING WITH THAT HAD WHEELS WAS _____

_____ .

I WAS _____ YEARS OLD WHEN I LEARNED TO RIDE A TWO-WHEELED BIKE. WHAT

I REMEMBER MOST ABOUT IT IS _____ .

WHEN YOUR DAD AND I WERE FIRST MARRIED, OUR CAR WAS A _____ .

ONE EXPERIENCE I RECALL ABOUT THAT CAR IS _____

_____ .

YOUR FAVORITE SET OF WHEELS AS A CHILD WAS _____

YOU LEARNED HOW TO RIDE A TWO-WHEELED BIKE BY _____ .

I GOT MY DRIVER'S LICENSE WHEN I WAS _____ ,

AND _____ TAUGHT ME HOW TO DRIVE. THE HARDEST THING I

REMEMBER ABOUT FIRST LEARNING TO DRIVE WAS _____ .

WATCHING YOU LEARN TO DRIVE WAS _____ FOR YOUR DAD

AND ME. MY STRONGEST MEMORY ABOUT IT IS _____

_____ .

ONCE YOU HAD YOUR DRIVER'S LICENSE AND COULD TAKE THE CAR ON YOUR OWN, I

FELT _____ .

Keepsakes

Everyone needs a scrapbook or memento box. In it you keep the tokens that symbolize important moments and people. With the passing of time, certain objects become less important and others take their place. Some experiences, though, we want to mark forever. We keep mementos from them in boxes, to be sorted through every so often when the spirit moves us.

My mother used to collect _____.

When I was a child, my most secret hiding place for special things that I

didn't want anyone else to find was _____.

Some of the keepsakes I still have from my childhood are _____

_____.

From my high school prom, I have my _____.

I exchanged _____ with my "steady" in high

school.

My favorite memento of your father's and my romance is _____.

Something I've kept that always reminds me of a dear friend is _____

_____.

Some people keep their treasures in a jar, a box, or a scrapbook. My favorite

way to keep things that are important to me is in a _____.

I still have the program for _____, the

performance was so memorable. I was particularly impressed by _____

_____.

I've saved some things to remind me of your childhood. You'll be surprised to

find out that I've saved _____.

Things you used to save when you were little include _____.

Gifts and Tokens

When my grandmother died, I was given her piano. It is the one thing I'd never get rid of. I still remember Grandma playing at family gatherings while others sang. She would get a sweet smile on her face and a happy twinkle in her eye, and you just knew that having her family sing together was one of her greatest pleasures. It would have pleased Grandma that not only did her granddaughter learn to play on her lovely piano, but her great-grandchildren did, too. How many hands and fingers this old piano has seen!

THESE THINGS HAVE BEEN HANDED DOWN IN MY FAMILY, AND YOU'LL HAVE THEM SOME

DAY: _____

_____.

A GIFT MY MOTHER GAVE ME THAT I STILL HAVE IS _____.

WHENEVER I LOOK AT IT, I'M REMINDED OF _____.

A TOKEN OF FRIENDSHIP I WAS ONCE GIVEN THAT I STILL HOLD DEAR IS _____

_____.

THE MOST ROMANTIC THING ANYONE HAS EVER GIVEN ME IS _____

_____.

AN ENGAGEMENT RING IS A TOKEN OF LOVE AND A GIFT SIGNIFYING THE INTENT TO

MARRY. THE STORY SURROUNDING MY ENGAGEMENT RING IS _____

_____

_____.

THE FIRST PRESENT YOU EVER GAVE ME IS _____.

ONE OF YOUR FAVORITE CHILDHOOD BIRTHDAY PRESENTS WAS _____.

YOUR BEST FRIEND ONCE GAVE YOU A _____.

WE GAVE YOU _____ FOR A GRADUATION GIFT.

THE MOST SIGNIFICANT GIFT YOU'VE RECEIVED IS _____.

EVERLASTING MEMORIES

Important Firsts

Even if you repeat an experience again and again, the first time holds a special place in memory. To remain young as the years unfold, make sure the new beginnings never end. If you continually take new steps, your life will remain vibrant and unpredictable, bringing the very ingredients for excitement and joy. I've lived through many "firsts," yours and mine. I expect we'll both have many, many more.

My earliest childhood memory is _____

_____.

My first date was _____.

My first job was _____.

The day you took your first steps was _____.

We celebrated your first birthday by _____.

Do you remember your first

Pet? _____

High heels? _____

Meal you cooked by yourself? _____

Boy-girl party? _____

Night away from home? _____

Dance? _____

Trip alone? _____

Money you earned? _____

A journey of a thousand miles

begins with one step.

Chinese proverb

Weddings

Whenever I attend a wedding, I cry. It's the sheer grandeur and importance of it all— the absolute beauty of two people pledging to stand by the side of each other for a lifetime. When I said those words, my lips quivered and I had to hold back the tears. I wasn't frightened or sad—I was so happy I could barely speak and so filled with emotion there wasn't anything else to do but let it overflow. On your wedding day, I felt content that you had found this fulfilling relationship.

MY PARENTS FIRST MET IN _____.

THEY WERE MARRIED IN THE YEAR _____. MY MOTHER'S ENGAGEMENT RING

WAS _____. HER WEDDING DRESS WAS _____.

WHAT MOST ATTRACTED ME TO YOUR FATHER WAS _____

_____.

THE MOMENT I KNEW I WANTED TO SPEND THE REST OF MY LIFE WITH YOUR DAD WAS

WHEN _____.

YOUR DAD PROPOSED TO ME _____.

MY ENGAGEMENT RING WAS _____.

WE WERE MARRIED IN _____ IN THE YEAR _____.

ON OUR WEDDING DAY, THE WEATHER WAS _____.

MY MAID OF HONOR WAS _____, AND THE BRIDESMAIDS

WERE _____

_____.

There is only one happiness in life,
to love and be loved.

George Sand

THE BEST MAN WAS _____, AND THE GROOMSMEN

WERE _____

_____ .

MY WEDDING DRESS WAS _____ .

THE MUSIC THAT WAS PLAYED DURING THE CEREMONY WAS _____

_____ .

WE SPENT OUR HONEYMOON IN _____ .

I KNEW YOU AND _____ WERE DESTINED TO BE MARRIED WHEN

_____

_____ .

YOUR FATHER AND I AGREED THAT YOUR FUTURE SPOUSE WAS _____

_____ .

YOU WERE MARRIED IN _____ IN THE YEAR _____ .

THE MAID OF HONOR WAS _____ , AND

THE BEST MAN WAS _____ .

I THOUGHT THE BRIDE'S WEDDING DRESS WAS _____ .

WHAT I MOST REMEMBER ABOUT THE CEREMONY AND RECEPTION IS _____

_____.

YOU PLANNED _____ *FOR YOUR HONEYMOON.*

FAVORITE WEDDING PHOTOGRAPH

When I was born, I was so surprised I couldn't talk for a year and a half.

Gracie Allen

Wee Beginnings

On the day you were born, your father and I drove to the hospital both excited and nervous. What will it look like? Will it have hair? Will it cry a lot or just coo and sleep? Will I be a good mother? Will I know what to do? All the questions were buried in the work of bringing you into the world and the wonder of your being. The little fingers and toes—they actually MOVED! It makes noise! It seems to be looking at us! The main tasks remaining were enjoying each other's presence and getting acquainted. Welcome, wee one. We're just getting started!

I WAS BORN IN _____.

WHEN MY MOTHER TOLD ME THE STORY OF MY BIRTH, SHE SAID _____

_____.

WHEN I TOLD YOUR FATHER I WAS PREGNANT WITH YOU, HIS REACTION WAS _____

_____.

IF YOU WERE A BOY, WE THOUGHT ABOUT NAMING YOU _____.

IF YOU WERE A GIRL, WE THOUGHT ABOUT NAMING YOU _____.

WHEN IT WAS TIME TO GO TO THE HOSPITAL, HE _____

_____.

YOU WERE BORN IN _____.

THE DAY YOU WERE BORN, THE WEATHER WAS _____.

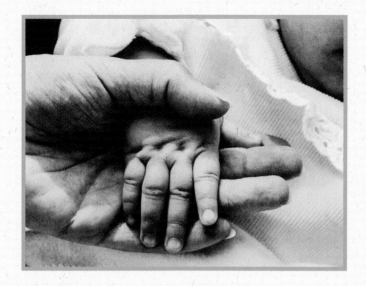

What feeling is so nice as a child's hand in yours? So small, so soft and warm, like a kitten huddling in the shelter of your clasp.

Marjorie Holmes

WE NAMED YOU _____ , BECAUSE _____

_____ .

THE FIRST TIME I SAW YOU, MY VERY FIRST THOUGHT WAS _____

_____ .

WHEN YOUR FATHER FIRST SAW YOU, HIS REACTION WAS _____

_____ .

SOME OF THE PEOPLE WHO CAME TO SEE YOU IN THE HOSPITAL WERE _____

_____ .

PEOPLE SAID YOU LOOKED LIKE _____.

MANY PEOPLE SENT YOU GIFTS. SOME OF THEM WERE _____

_____.

THE DAY WE TOOK YOU HOME, I DRESSED YOU IN _____.

WHAT I REMEMBER MOST ABOUT THAT DAY IS _____

_____.

THE FIRST DAY WE WERE ALL HOME TOGETHER, IT WAS _____

_____.

A FAVORITE BABY PHOTO

Rest and Recreation

The way we spend our leisure time says much about who we really are. Some people like to be busy, initiating projects, volunteering their time, making improvements in their home, taking up hobbies. Some people use every available chance to get into the great outdoors, hiking, camping, boating, and learning about our many animal friends. Still others like to retreat into themselves, reading and spending time in solitude, perhaps involving themselves in something creative like writing or painting. I enjoy all of these, depending on exactly what my spirit needs most.

I REMEMBER MY MOTHER SPENDING MANY HOURS _____.

WHEN MY FATHER WANTED TO RELAX, HE _____.

WHEN OUR FAMILY PLAYED GAMES, WE PLAYED _____.

AS A CHILD, MY FAVORITE HOBBY WAS _____.

IN SCHOOL, MY FAVORITE SPORTS TO PARTICIPATE IN WERE _____.

SPORTS I ENJOY WATCHING ARE _____.

SOMETIME IN THE FUTURE I'D LIKE TO TAKE UP _____.

CRAFTS YOU ENJOYED AS A CHILD WERE _____.

WINTER ACTIVITIES YOU ALWAYS ENJOYED WERE _____.

YOUR FAVORITE SUMMERTIME ACTIVITIES WERE _____.

YOUR OUTSTANDING SCHOOL ACTIVITIES WERE _____.

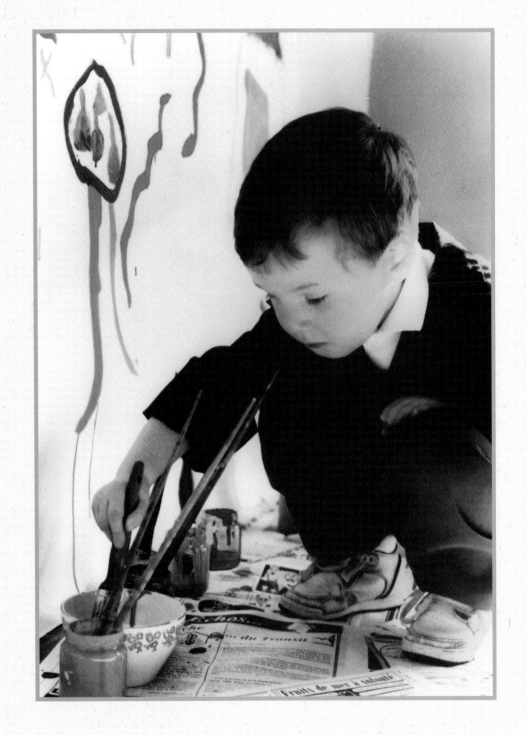

One ought, every day at least, to hear a little song, read a good poem, see a fine picture, and, if it were possible, to speak a few reasonable words.

Johann W. von Goethe

49

Responsibilities

When I was only four, I was already being assigned chores. I was expected to put away my clothes, help with the dusting, and even work alongside my parents in the garden. As I got older, we kids shared the tasks of setting the table and clearing it after a meal. Though we'd rather have been outside playing after dinner on a summer evening, we took pride in a finished chore. When you were growing up, you had your chores, too. Remember the charts on the refrigerator listing everybody's things to do for the week? And the gold foil stars you got at the end? When you got older, the stars turned into quarters that were plunked into a piggy bank for some important purchase.

Always do right. This will gratify some people, and astonish the rest.

Mark Twain

MY MOTHER'S RESPONSIBILITIES IN OUR FAMILY WERE _____

_____.

MY FATHER'S RESPONSIBILITIES WERE _____

_____.

I LEARNED MY EARLY LESSONS ABOUT MONEY THROUGH _____.

SOME OF MY HOUSEHOLD CHORES WERE _____.

IN OUR FAMILY, PETS WERE TAKEN CARE OF BY _____.

MY FIRST BANK ACCOUNT WAS _____.

MY FIRST CHARGE ACCOUNT WAS _____. I REACTED TO

GETTING A CHARGE ACCOUNT BY _____.

WHEN YOU WERE LITTLE, I GAVE YOU THE CHORES OF _____

_____.

THE FIRST MONEY YOU EVER HAD OF YOUR OWN WAS _____.

YOUR FATHER AND I REQUIRED YOU TO SAVE FOR _____.

RESPONSIBILITIES YOU ACCEPTED AT SCHOOL INCLUDE _____

_____.

YOU HAVE SHOWN A TRUE SENSE OF RESPONSIBILITY BY _____

_____.

Rituals and Traditions

Some of my favorite rituals or traditions are those surrounding the changing of the seasons. On the first truly springlike day, when you could just feel the tulips and lilacs getting ready to bloom, I would buy an armful of daffodils and spread them in vases all through the house. Next, I would play an old, worn recording of Schumann's Spring Symphony. I'd turn up the volume and throw the windows open, as if I were greeting spring and bidding her to stay. All the bedding would come off—pillows, blankets, quilts— and be hung in the fresh air and sunshine on the backyard clothesline. You could tell by the smell of your pillow that night that spring, no doubt, had sprung!

HERE ARE SOME OF OUR FAMILY TRADITIONS FOR CELEBRATING

NEW YEAR'S EVE AND NEW YEAR'S DAY _____

_____

_____.

VALENTINE'S DAY _____

_____.

EASTER OR PASSOVER _____

_____

_____.

MOTHER'S DAY _____

_____.

FATHER'S DAY _____

_____.

MEMORIAL DAY _____

_____.

FOURTH OF JULY _____

_____.

LABOR DAY _____.

HALLOWEEN _____
_____
_____.

THANKSGIVING _____
_____
_____.

CHRISTMAS OR HANUKKAH _____
_____
_____.

MY FAVORITE HOLIDAY IS _____, BECAUSE
_____.

WHEN YOU WERE LITTLE, YOUR FAVORITE HOLIDAY CELEBRATION WAS _____
_____. I KNEW THIS BECAUSE
_____.

HOLIDAY DECORATIONS AND ORNAMENTS HANDED DOWN FROM MY FAMILY AND YOUR

FATHER'S FAMILY ARE _____
_____
_____.

OUR TRADITIONAL BIRTHDAY RITUALS INCLUDE _____

_____ .

OUR HOLIDAY CELEBRATIONS WERE USUALLY SPENT AT _____ .

YOUR FAVORITE BIRTHDAY CAKE WAS _____ , AND YOU ALWAYS

REQUESTED _____ FOR YOUR BIRTHDAY DINNER.

AS A FAMILY, WE'VE DEVELOPED OUR OWN TRADITIONS FOR _____ .

WHEN A CHILD LOSES A TOOTH, WE _____ .

THE FIRST TIME THAT HAPPENED TO YOU, YOU _____ .

AT LEAST ONCE DURING THE SUMMER, WE ALWAYS _____ .

AT LEAST ONCE DURING THE WINTER, WE ALWAYS _____ .

I'D LIKE TO START A NEW CELEBRATION OR TRADITION OF _____

_____ .

The holiest of all holidays are those
Kept by ourselves in silence and apart;
The secret anniversaries of the heart.

Henry Wadsworth Longfellow

55

*A little garden in which to walk, an immensity in which to dream, at one's feet that which can
be cultivated and plucked; overhead that which one can study and meditate upon;
some herbs on earth and all the stars in the sky.*

Victor Hugo

Guiding Experiences

Most of us spend our lives searching for an inner life larger than ourselves. I find my spiritual peace in nature. The never-ending spectacle of the natural world reminds me how little I know, how wondrous the mystery is, and how much is yet to be revealed. Treat your inner life as a garden, to be planted, watered, nurtured, and enjoyed, which when properly tended will yield the greatest rewards.

MY MOTHER TOLD ME SHE HAD BEEN INSPIRED BY _____

_____.

HER STRONGEST VALUES WERE _____

_____.

MY EARLIEST INSPIRATION CAME FROM _____

_____.

MILESTONES IN MY SPIRITUAL LIFE INCLUDE _____

_____.

I FELT I HAD BECOME A STRONGER PERSON AFTER MY EXPERIENCE OF _____

_____.

READING _____ MADE A PROFOUND

IMPRESSION ON ME.

I AM ALWAYS MOVED BY THE SIGHT OF _____.

A Place in History

The span of every life, no matter when it begins, encompasses so many profound events and so many incredible changes. Not just new inventions, but changes in the way people behave and think. When I recall the time when I was a girl, I realize that the everyday lives of both women and men were different then. And you don't realize at the time that one day this everyday life would be part of "history." It's only during the extraordinary events that you realize you're part of history.

WHEN MY MOTHER WAS A YOUNG WOMAN, SHE WORE _____.

SHE WAS EXPECTED TO BE _____ *WHEN SHE*

GREW UP.

IN THOSE DAYS, PEOPLE'S CHIEF FORM OF ENTERTAINMENT WAS _____

_____.

AN IMPORTANT EVENT THAT MY MOTHER REMEMBERED IS _____

_____.

LITTLE GIRLS WORE _____ *TO SCHOOL*

WHEN I WAS YOUNG.

THE BIGGEST DIFFERENCE BETWEEN THE WORLD OF MY YOUTH AND TODAY IS _____

_____.

I CAN REMEMBER BEFORE WE HAD _____

_____.

THE INVENTION THAT HAS MOST CHANGED MY LIFE IS _____.

ONE OF THE MOST IMPORTANT EVENTS THAT I CAN REMEMBER IS _____

_____.

SOMETHING I NEVER THOUGHT I'D SEE IN MY LIFETIME THAT HAS ALREADY OCCURRED IS

_____.

FEELINGS AND FANCIES

Precious Moments

A life has shining moments, pieces of time frozen for always, that shimmer from the past into the present. They take on a richer patina as they age, like fine silver, as we polish them and keep them forever bright. These moments might not be great events or rites of passage, but simply experiences when we are intensely aware of the joy of life. I'd like to share some of these precious moments with you now.

My favorite memory from childhood is _____

_____ .

I felt closest to my mother when _____

_____ .

I was proudest of myself when _____

_____ .

The biggest surprise I ever got was _____

_____ .

My favorite memory about you is _____

_____ .

I felt myself bursting with pride when you _____

_____ .

I knew you were a grown-up when you _____

_____ .

Backward, turn backward, O Time, in your flight,
Make me a child again just for tonight!

Elizabeth Akers Allen

Favorites

*S*o many little things delight us and become our favorite things. If we have these favorites to turn to, the ups and downs of life are easier to bear. One of my favorite aromas is that of fresh flowers. I love to place a small vase of fresh flowers in the bedroom. As I drift off to sleep, their beautiful aroma makes me think I am going to rest in a garden. How can I help having anything but sweet dreams?

MY MOTHER'S FAVORITES:

COLOR _____

SEASON _____

HOLIDAY _____

MY FAVORITES:

BOOK _____

FOOD _____

FLOWER _____

YOUR FAVORITES:

SONG _____

MOVIE _____

DESSERT _____

It isn't the great big pleasures that
count the most; it's making a great
deal out of the little ones.

Jean Webster

Achievements

Achievements have rewards, it's true, but the greatest reward is the journey toward the goal. If the process itself isn't worthwhile, then neither is the achievement. Something in the human heart thrives on struggle and overcoming obstacles. Those achievements are sweetest that took the greatest effort. Always set goals that seem just beyond your reach. Don't go for the brass ring you know you can grab with ease. And make sure the goals you choose to work toward are important to you and you alone. Pleasing others is futile and a sure road to unhappiness. Know your own heart and believe in yourself.

You must do the thing you think you
cannot do.

Eleanor Roosevelt

MY MOTHER'S GREATEST ACCOMPLISHMENT WAS _____

_____ .

THE GREATEST HONOR MY FATHER RECEIVED WAS _____

_____ .

AS A CHILD, MY GREATEST ACHIEVEMENT WAS _____

_____ .

THE HARDEST THING I'VE EVER HAD TO DO WAS _____

_____ .

MY FINEST ACCOMPLISHMENT WAS _____

_____ .

MY GOALS FOR THE FUTURE ARE _____

_____ .

THE ACHIEVEMENT OF YOURS THAT MEANS THE MOST TO ME IS _____

_____ .

Those who dare to fail miserably
can achieve greatly.

Robert F. Kennedy

Imagination is the highest kite
one can fly.

Lauren Bacall

Pretending

$\mathcal{F}$or a child, pretending is an integral part of life. Fairy tales and nursery rhymes are cherished from generation to generation because they feed the imagination. Even as grown-ups we need a form of pretending. Imagination, dreams, and fantasies fuel our achievements, add richness to our relationships, entertain us, and give us comfort in times of trouble. Remain a child in the best sense of the word and never cease pretending.

WHEN I WAS LITTLE, MY FAVORITE FAIRY TALE WAS _____.

AFTER I LEARNED TO READ, MY FAVORITE BOOK WAS _____.

I USED TO PRETEND I WAS _____.

MY FRIENDS AND I USED TO PLAY _____.

THE ROLE I USUALLY TOOK WAS _____.

TODAY I OFTEN DAYDREAM ABOUT _____.

MY FANTASY CAREER WOULD BE _____.

THE BEDTIME STORY YOU COULD LISTEN TO OVER AND OVER WAS _____.

YOUR FAVORITE FAIRY TALE WAS _____.

YOU USED TO LIKE TO DRESS UP AS _____.

YOU PLAYED _____ IN A SCHOOL PLAY.

Words of Love

Never underestimate the impact that words have. Words can sting or soothe, tear down or build up, confuse or communicate. I hope you will be surrounded by words that teach, inspire, and encourage you, and I implore you to speak and write words that do the same for others. Some words we always understand—words of love and approval, words of comfort and understanding. The words "I love you" are the most powerful words in the English language.

Good words are worth much, and cost little.

George Herbert

LIKE ALL FAMILIES, OURS HAS ITS OWN SAYINGS. SOME OF THEM ARE _____

_____ .

THE NICKNAME I WAS KNOWN BY AS A CHILD WAS _____ .

SPECIAL NAMES WE HAVE FOR EXTENDED FAMILY MEMBERS ARE _____

_____ .

WHEN YOU WERE A BABY, WE CALLED YOU _____ .

THE NICEST THING ANYBODY EVER SAID TO ME WAS _____

_____ .

SOME INSPIRATIONAL WORDS I REMEMBER ARE _____

_____ .

ONE OF MY FAVORITE QUOTATIONS IS _____

_____ .

Lessons Learned

I used to think when I grew up I'd know everything. All the mysteries of the universe would be revealed. When I finally got there, I discovered that not only did I not know everything, but no one else did, either! The more I learned, the more I realized how much I didn't know. Now I see that life is a series of lessons. I hope your father and I have helped teach you some of the more valuable ones.

THE MOST IMPORTANT LESSON MY PARENTS TAUGHT ME WAS _____

_____.

THE MOST IMPORTANT LESSON I LEARNED FROM BEING A PARENT HAS BEEN _____

_____.

ASIDE FROM THE SUBJECTS TAUGHT, I LEARNED _____

_____ FROM BEING IN SCHOOL.

ONE MENTOR I HAD WHEN I WAS YOUNG WAS _____,

WHO TAUGHT ME _____.

THE BEST ADVICE I'VE EVER RECEIVED WAS _____

_____.

THE HARDEST LESSON I'VE HAD TO LEARN IS _____

_____.

ONE IMPORTANT LESSON I'D LIKE TO PASS ON IS _____

_____.

Knowledge is proud that he has learned so much;
Wisdom is humble that he knows no more.

William Cowper

71

YOUR FAMILY TREE

Your mother

_____

You

_____

Your father

_____

72

Your mother's mother

_____

Your mother's maternal
grandparents

_____

_____

Your mother's father

_____

Your mother's paternal
grandparents

_____

_____

Your father's mother

_____

Your father's maternal
grandparents

_____

Your father's father

_____

Your father's paternal
grandparents

_____

_____

73